# Presentation Workbook 2

プレゼンワークブック

2nd Edition

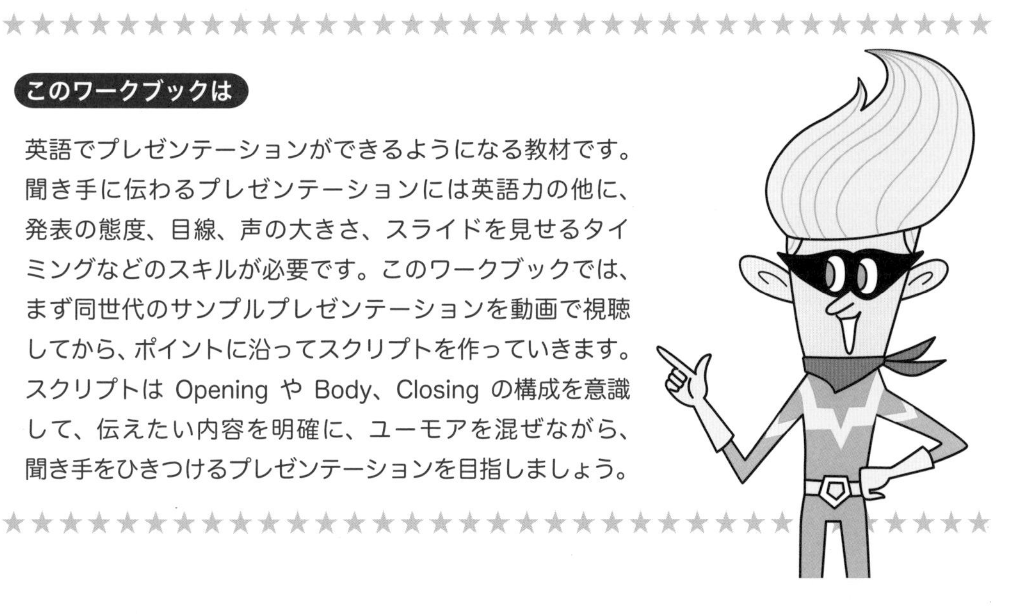

**このワークブックは**

英語でプレゼンテーションができるようになる教材です。聞き手に伝わるプレゼンテーションには英語力の他に、発表の態度、目線、声の大きさ、スライドを見せるタイミングなどのスキルが必要です。このワークブックでは、まず同世代のサンプルプレゼンテーションを動画で視聴してから、ポイントに沿ってスクリプトを作っていきます。スクリプトは Opening や Body、Closing の構成を意識して、伝えたい内容を明確に、ユーモアを混ぜながら、聞き手をひきつけるプレゼンテーションを目指しましょう。

## Contents

# このワークブックの使い方

## はじめに

聞き手に伝わるプレゼンに
必要なポイントを確認しよう!

pp.4-7

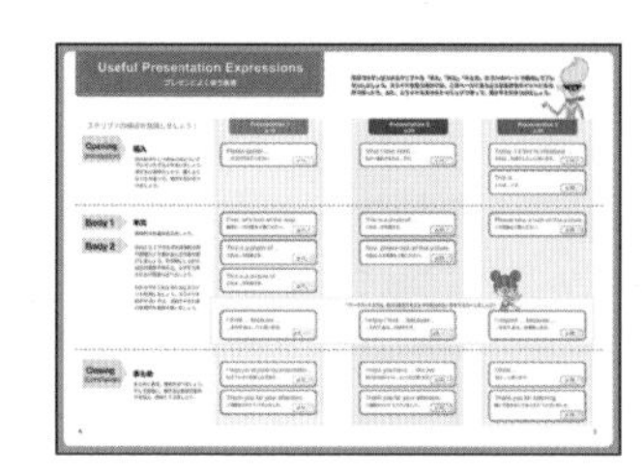


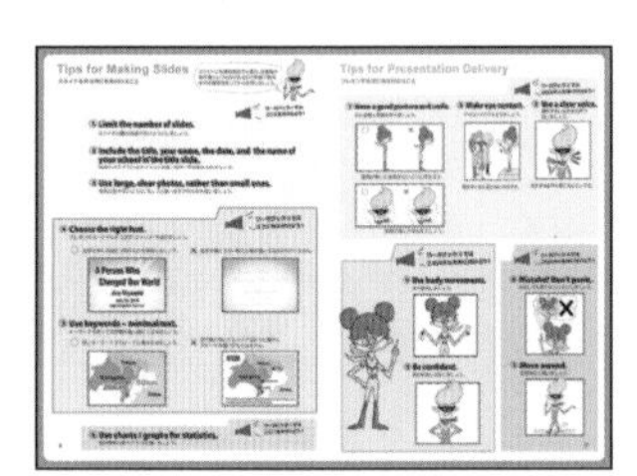


## Presentation 1～3 の構成と進め方

### Step 1 Watch it! 動画のサンプルプレゼンを見よう！

まずは、動画のサンプル
プレゼンを見てみよう。

動画のサンプルプレゼンで
使用されたスライドです。

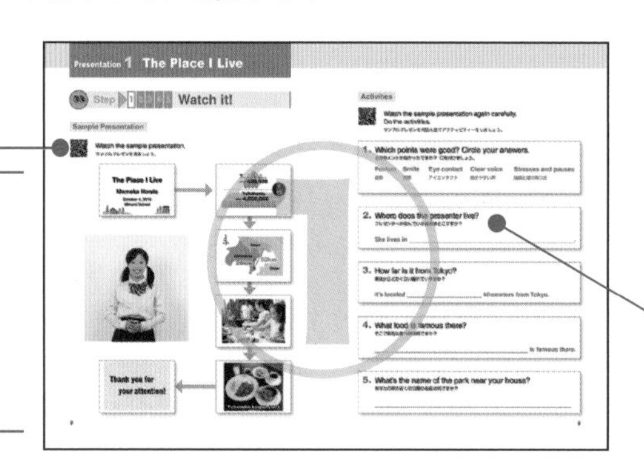


何度もサンプルプレゼンを
見て、プレゼンの内容やプ
レゼンターの態度に関する
質問に答えよう。

### Step 2 Write it! 自分のプレゼンについてメモしよう！

サンプルリーディングを動画で
見ながら、声に出してまねして
言ってみよう。

青い文字は Useful Presentation
Expressions(pp.4-5) で紹介され
ているフレーズです。

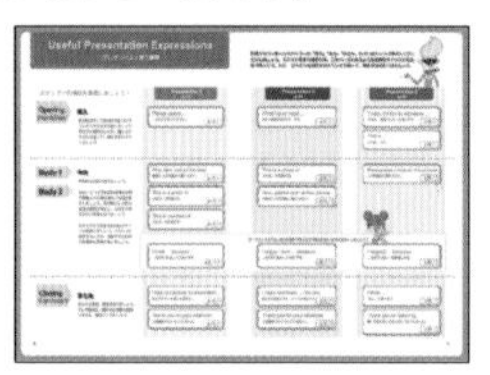


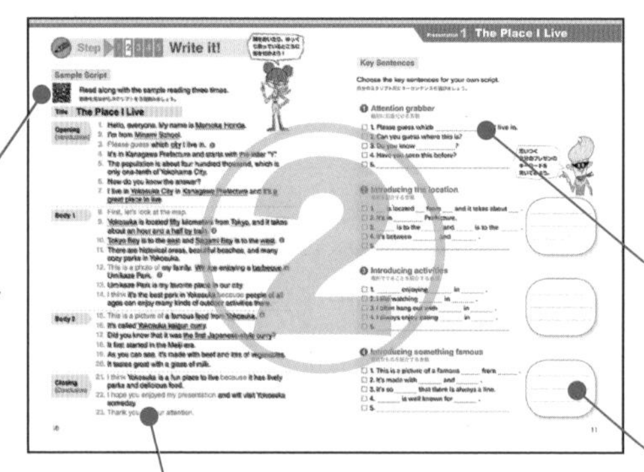


当てはまるものに✔を付け
てみよう。なければ、自分
で考えて線の上に書いてみ
よう。

思いつくキーワードを
書いておこう。

下線の所は、自分のことにあてはまる
文章に置きかえよう。

### Step 3 Design it! 自分のプレゼンを作ろう！

まず、自分が見せるスライドの
イメージを手描きしよう。
その次に実際にコンピューター
でスライドを作ろう。

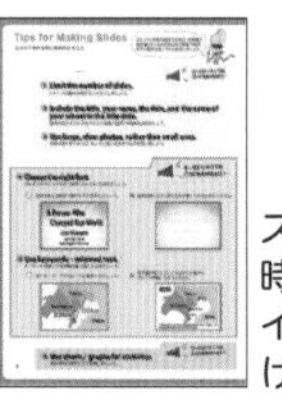


スライドを作る
時には p.6 のポ
イントに気を付
けよう。

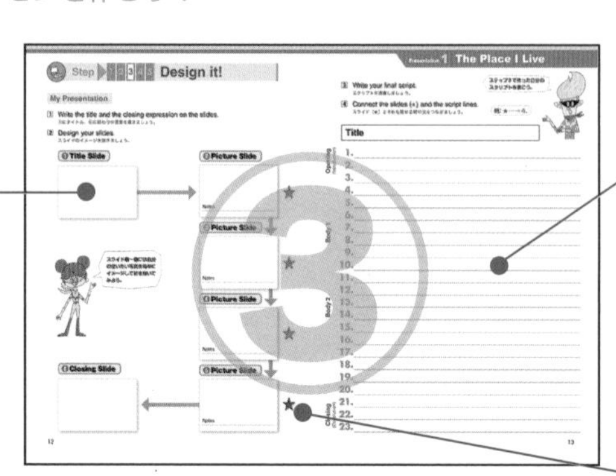


Write it! でメモした事をもと
自分のプレゼンのスクリプト
清書しよう。

自分のスクリプトができた
スクリプトの文章とスライ
を線でつないで、スライド
見せるタイミングを決めよう

## Step 4 Present it! プレゼンをするための準備をしよう！

プレゼンのスクリプトを暗記するためにキーワードやアイコンを描いてスクリプトを覚えよう。

プレゼンをする時に必要な態度（p.7）を練習しよう。

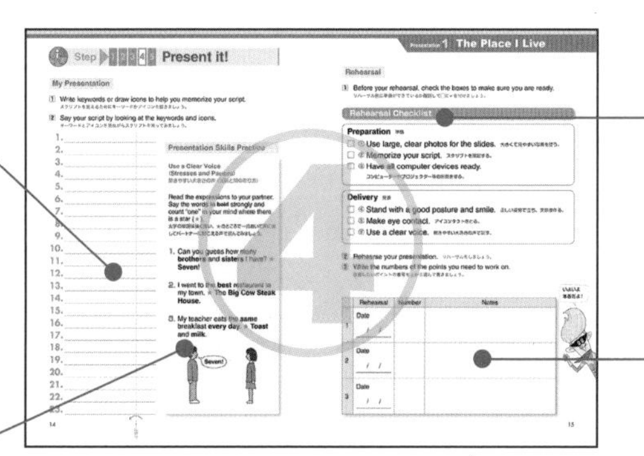

発表前に必ずリハーサルをしよう。リハーサルの準備は整ったか、チェックリストで確認しよう。

リハーサルを最低3回はしよう。リハーサルの改善点に気を付けて、本番にチャレンジしよう。

## Step 5 Evaluate it! プレゼンが終わったら、振り返りをしよう！

プレゼンの本番が終わったら、自分の反省点や聞き手の感想、先生のコメントを記入しよう。

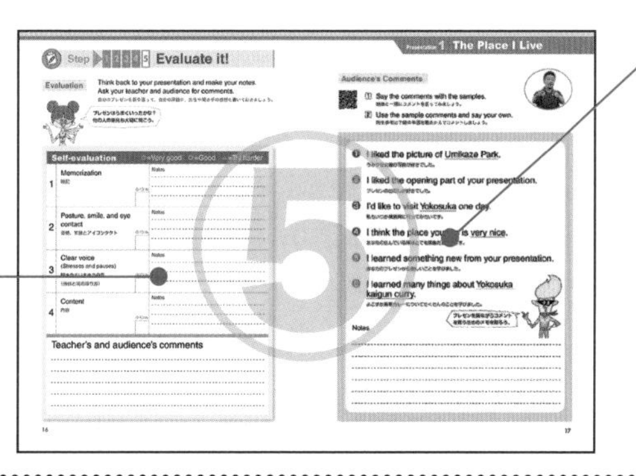

他の人のプレゼンを見終ったら、英語でコメントを言えるようになろう。動画のサンプルを見ながらコメントの練習をしよう。

他の人のプレゼンを見終わったら、p.47 の表に記録をしておこう。

## Presentation 4 Make Your Own の構成と進め方

Presentation 4 では自分で自由にトピックを選んでプレゼンしよう。

### Step 1 Plan it! トピックを考えてプランを作ろう！

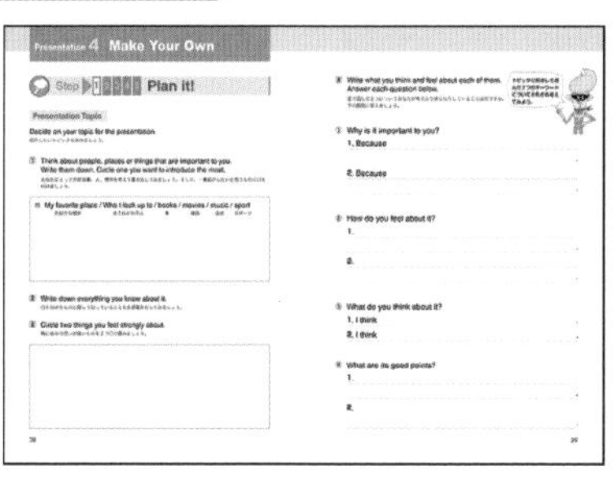

### Step 2 Write it! プランを元にスクリプトを書こう！

Step 3 Step 4 Step 5 は Presentation 1～3 と同じように進めよう。

## 質問力を上げよう！ Poster Session・Basic

プレゼンで作ったスライドを使って
ポスターセッションをやってみよう。

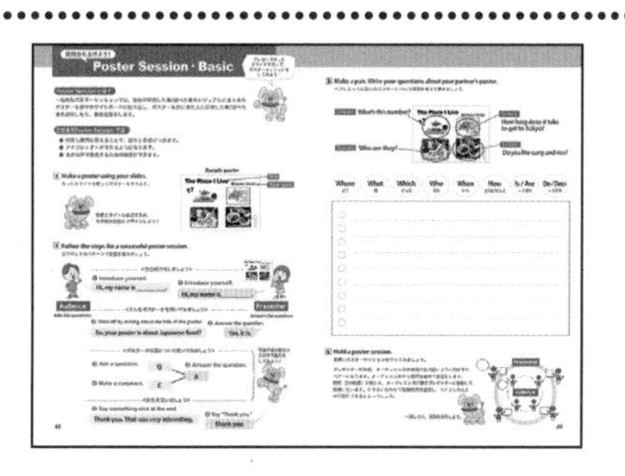

# Useful Presentation Expressions

## プレゼンによく使う表現

スクリプトの構成を意識しましょう！

**Presentation 1**
**p.10**

### Opening (Introduction)

**導入**

自己紹介をして自分が何についてプレゼンをするかを言いましょう。聞き手に質問をしたり、驚くようなことを言って、聞き手をひきつけましょう。

Please guess ...
... を当ててみてください。
p.10_3

---

### Body 1

### Body 2

**本文**

具体的な内容を伝えましょう。

Body1 と 2 でそれぞれ具体的な例や経験などを盛り込んで内容を紹介しましょう。その時にしっかり、自分の意見や考えと、なぜそう考えたかの理由も述べましょう。

わかりやすく伝えるためにスライドを利用しましょう。スライドを紹介するときは、注目させるための効果的な表現を使いましょう。

First, let's look at the map.
最初に、この地図をご覧ください。
p.10_8

This is a photo of ...
これは ... の写真です。
p.10_12

This is a picture of ...
これは ... の写真です。
p.10_15

I think ... because ...
... なので、私は ... だと思います。
p.10_14/21

---

### Closing (Conclusion)

**まとめ**

まとめと意見、感想を述べましょう。そして最後に、聞き手に感謝の気持ちを伝え、締めくくりましょう。

I hope you enjoyed my presentation ...
私のプレゼンを楽しんで頂き ... といいなと思います。
p.10_22

Thank you for your attention.
ご清聴ありがとうございました。
p.10_23

英語でのプレゼンはスクリプトを「導入」「本文」「まとめ」の３つのパートで構成してプレゼンしましょう。スライドを使う場合には、このページにあるような表現をポイントになる所で使ったり、また、スライドを見せるタイミングで使って、聞き手を引きつけましょう。

## Presentation 2
p.20

What I love most ...
私が一番好きなのは ... です。
p.20_6

This is a photo of ...
これは ... の写真です。
p.20_8

Now, please look at this picture.
今度は、この写真をご覧ください。
p.20_13

I enjoy / love ... because ...
... なので、私は ... が好きです。
p.20_11/15

I hope you have ... like me.
あなたにも私のように ... といいなと思います。
p.20_21

Thank you for your attention.
ご清聴ありがとうございました。
p.20_22

## Presentation 3
p.30

Today, I'd like to introduce ...
今日は ... を紹介したいと思います。
p.30_6

This is ...
これは ... です。
p.30_7

Please take a look at this picture.
この写真をご覧ください。
p.30_13

I respect ... because ...
... なので、私は ... を尊敬します。
p.30_15

I think ...
私は ... と思います。
p.30_21

Thank you for listening.
聞いて頂きましてありがとうございました。
p.30_22

ークブック２では、自分の意見や考えとその理由の言い方をマスターしましょう!!

# Tips for Making Slides

## スライドを作る時に気を付けること

スライドに写真を使用する場合、肖像権や著作権というものがあるので無断で使用せずに確認を取ってから使用しましょう。

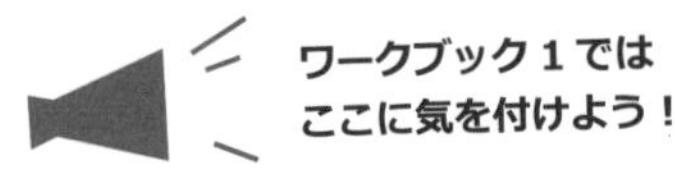


### ① Limit the number of slides.

スライドの数は多過ぎないようにしましょう。

### ② Include the title, your name, the date, and the name of your school in the title slide.

始めのスライドにはタイトル / 氏名 / 日付 / 学校名を入れましょう。

### ③ Use large, clear photos, rather than small ones.

写真は見やすいように、ちょうど良い大きさのものを使いましょう。

ワークブック２では
ここに気を付けよう！

### ④ Choose the right font.

プレゼンのスライドに合う文字（フォント）を選びましょう。

○ 文字は太くて目立つ色のものを使用しましょう。

A Person Who
Changed Our World
Jiro Miyazaki
July 25, 2016
mpi English School

× 文字が細くうすい色だと何が書いてあるかわかりません

A Person Who
Changed Our World
Jiro Miyazaki
July 25, 2016
mpi English School

### ⑤ Use keywords – minimal text.

キーワードを使って文字数を最小限にとどめましょう。

○ 短いキーワードでスピーチに集中させましょう。

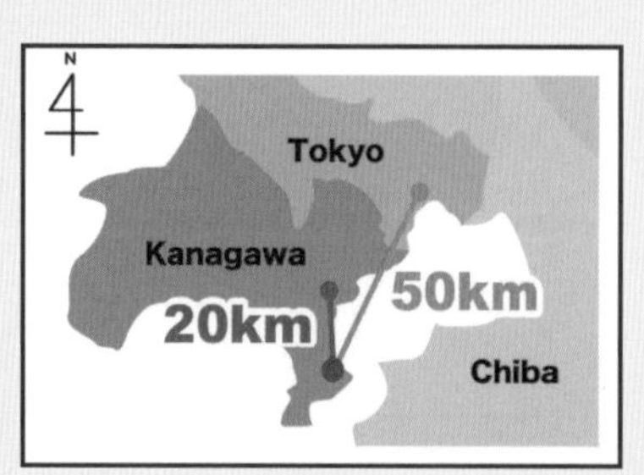


× 文字数が多いとスライドばかりに集中しスピーチを聞いてもらえません。

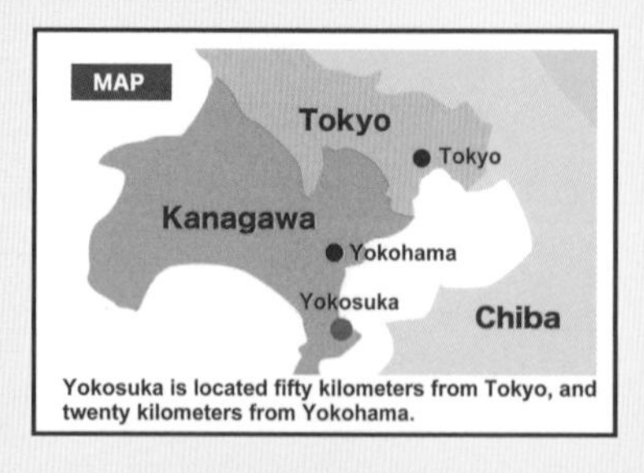


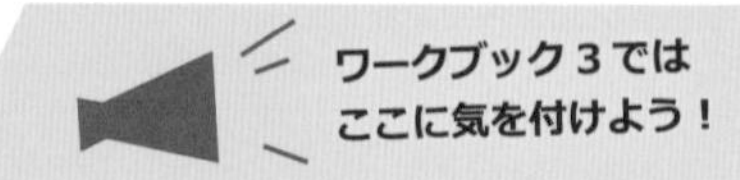


### ⑥ Use charts / graphs for statistics.

統計資料の表やグラフを使いましょう。

# Tips for Presentation Delivery

## プレゼンする時に気を付けること

ワークブック１では
このスキルを身に付けよう！

### ① Have a good posture and smile.

良い姿勢と笑顔を作りましょう。

姿勢が悪いと自信がないように見えます。

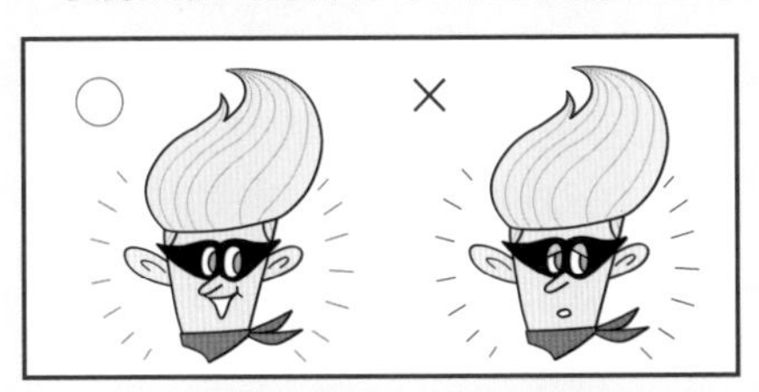

笑顔で楽しさを伝えましょう。

### ② Make eye contact.

アイコンタクトをとりましょう。

聞き手に伝えるために大切です。

### ③ Use a clear voice.

聞きやすい大きさの声で
話しましょう。

大きすぎる声も聞こえにくいです。

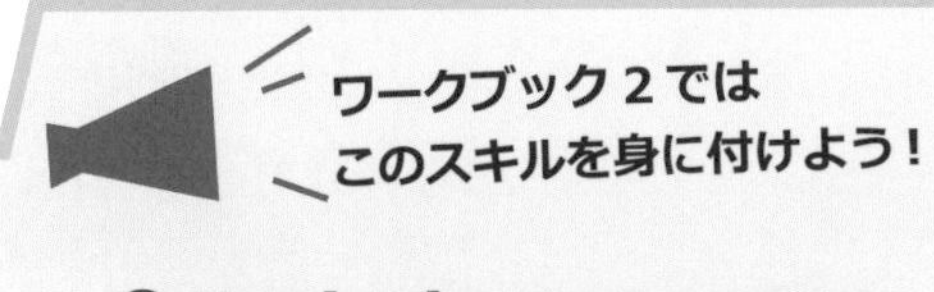


### ④ Use body movements.

体で表現しましょう。

### ⑤ Be confident.

自信を持って話しましょう。

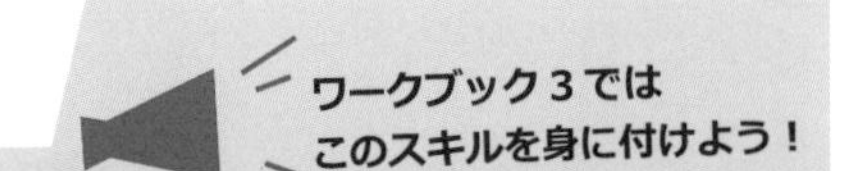


### ⑥ Mistake? Don't panic.

失敗しても慌てないようにしましょう。

### ⑦ Move around.

空間を広く使いましょう。

# Presentation 1 The Place I Live

## Step 1 2 3 4 5 Watch it!

### Sample Presentation

Watch the sample presentation.
サンプルプレゼンを見ましょう。

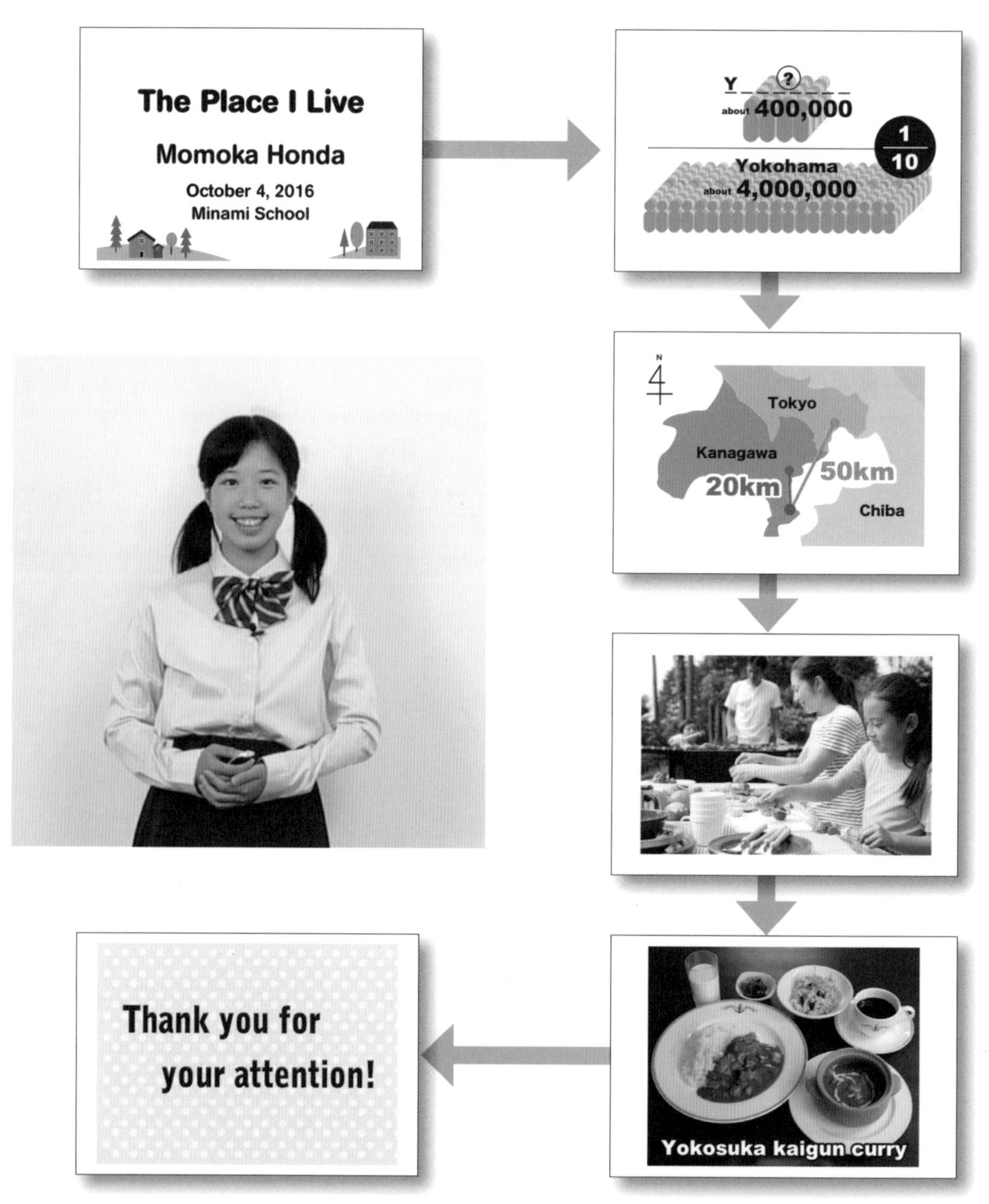

## Activities

Watch the sample presentation again carefully.
Do the activities.
サンプルプレゼンを何回も見てアクティビティーをしましょう。

**1.** Which points were good? Circle your answers.
どのポイントが良かったですか？ ○を付けましょう。

| Posture | Smile | Eye contact | Clear voice | Stresses and pauses |
|---|---|---|---|---|
| 姿勢 | 笑顔 | アイコンタクト | 聞きやすい声 | 強弱と間の取り方 |

**2.** Where does the presenter live?
プレゼンターが住んでいる場所はどこですか？

She lives in ______________________________.

**3.** How far is it from Tokyo?
東京からどのくらい離れていますか？

It's located ______________ kilometers from Tokyo.

**4.** What food is famous there?
そこで有名な食べ物は何ですか？

______________________________ is famous there.

**5.** What's the name of the park near your house?
あなたの家の近くの公園の名前は何ですか？

______________________________

# Step 1 2 3 4 5 Write it!

間をおいたり、ゆっくり言っているところに気を付けよう！

## Sample Script

Read along with the sample reading three times.
映像を見ながらスクリプトを３回読みましょう。

**Title** **The Place I Live**

**Opening** (Introduction)

1. Hello, everyone. My name is Momoka Honda.
2. I'm from Minami School.
3. Please guess which city I live in. ❶
4. It's in Kanagawa Prefecture and starts with the letter "Y".
5. The population is about four hundred thousand, which is only one-tenth of Yokohama City.
6. Now do you know the answer?
7. I live in Yokosuka City in Kanagawa Prefecture and it's a great place to live.

**Body 1**

8. First, let's look at the map.
9. Yokosuka is located fifty kilometers from Tokyo, and it takes about an hour and a half by train. ❷
10. Tokyo Bay is to the east and Sagami Bay is to the west. ❷
11. There are historical areas, beautiful beaches, and many cozy parks in Yokosuka.
12. This is a photo of my family. We are enjoying a barbeque in Umikaze Park. ❸
13. Umikaze Park is my favorite place in our city.
14. I think it's the best park in Yokosuka because people of all ages can enjoy many kinds of outdoor activities there.

**Body 2**

15. This is a picture of a famous food from Yokosuka. ❹
16. It's called Yokosuka kaigun curry.
17. Did you know that it was the first Japanese-style curry?
18. It first started in the Meiji era.
19. As you can see, it's made with beef and lots of vegetables.
20. It tastes great with a glass of milk.

**Closing** (Conclusion)

21. I think Yokosuka is a fun place to live because it has lively parks and delicious food.
22. I hope you enjoyed my presentation and will visit Yokosuka someday.
23. Thank you for your attention.

# Presentation 1 The Place I Live

## Key Sentences

Choose the key sentences for your own script.
自分のスクリプト用にキーセンテンスを選びましょう。

### ❶ Attention grabber
最初に印象付ける表現

- ☐ 1. Please guess which __________________ I live in.
- ☐ 2. Can you guess where this is?
- ☐ 3. Do you know ____________?
- ☐ 4. Have you seen this before?
- ☐ 5. __________________________________________

思いつく
自分のプレゼンの
キーワードを
書いてみよう。

### ❷ Introducing the location
場所を紹介する表現

- ☐ 1. ___ is located ___ from ___ and it takes about ___ .
- ☐ 2. It's in _________ Prefecture.
- ☐ 3. ______ is to the ______ and _____ is to the ______ .
- ☐ 4. It's between _______ and _______ .
- ☐ 5. __________________________________________

### ❸ Introducing activities
場所ですることを紹介する表現

- ☐ 1. _______ enjoying _______ in _______ .
- ☐ 2. I like watching _______ in _______ .
- ☐ 3. I often hang out with _______ in _______ .
- ☐ 4. I always enjoy eating _______ in _______ .
- ☐ 5. __________________________________________

### ❹ Introducing something famous
有名なものを紹介する表現

- ☐ 1. This is a picture of a famous ______ from ______ .
- ☐ 2. It's made with _______ and _______ .
- ☐ 3. It's so _______ that there is always a line.
- ☐ 4. _______ is well known for _______ .
- ☐ 5. __________________________________________

# Design it!

## My Presentation

1 Write the title and the closing expression on the slides.
①にタイトル、⑥に終わりの言葉を書きましょう。

2 Design your slides.
スライドのイメージを描きましょう。

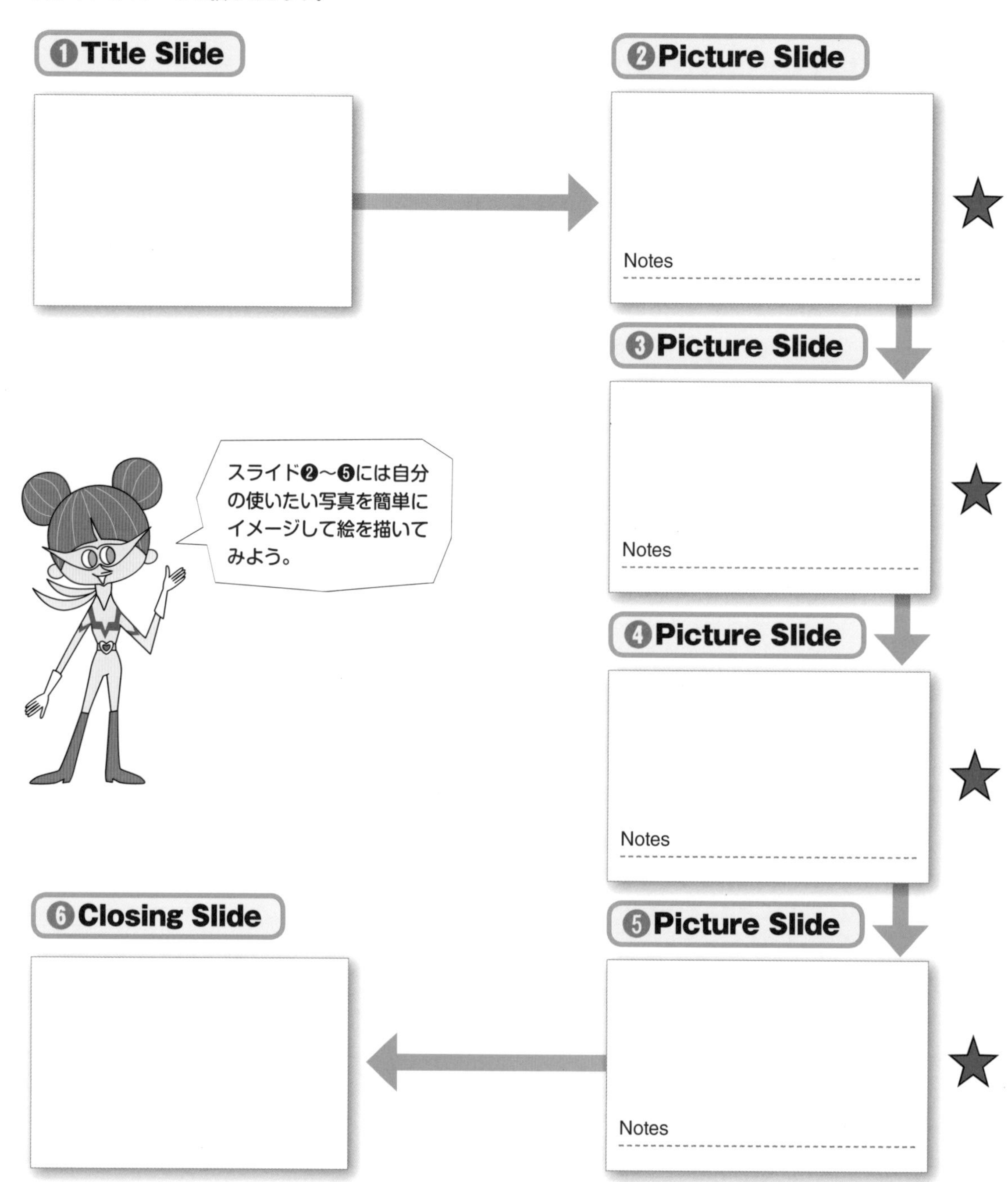

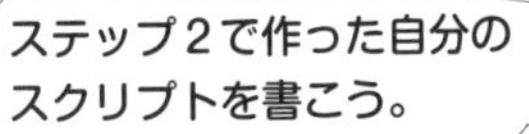
ステップ2で作った自分の
スクリプトを書こう。

3 Write your final script.
スクリプトを清書しましょう。

4 Connect the slides (★) and the script lines.
スライド（★）とそれを見せる時の文をつなぎましょう。

例：★ ⟶ 4.

**Title** ______

**Opening** (Introduction)

1. ______
2. ______
3. ______

**Body 1**

4. ______
5. ______
6. ______
7. ______
8. ______
9. ______
10. ______
11. ______
12. ______

**Body 2**

13. ______
14. ______
15. ______
16. ______
17. ______
18. ______
19. ______
20. ______

**Closing** (Conclusion)

21. ______
22. ______
23. ______

# Present it!

## My Presentation

1 Write keywords or draw icons to help you memorize your script.
スクリプトを覚えるためにキーワードかアイコンを描きましょう。

2 Say your script by looking at the keywords and icons.
キーワードとアイコンを見ながらスクリプトを言ってみましょう。

1. ____________
2. ____________
3. ____________
4. ____________
5. ____________
6. ____________
7. ____________
8. ____________
9. ____________
10. ____________
11. ____________
12. ____________
13. ____________
14. ____________
15. ____________
16. ____________
17. ____________
18. ____________
19. ____________
20. ____________
21. ____________
22. ____________
23. ____________

↑山折り

## Presentation Skills Practice

### Use a Clear Voice (Stresses and Pauses)
聞きやすい大きさの声（強弱と間の取り方）

Read the expressions to your partner. Say the words in **bold** strongly and count "one" in your mind where there is a star (★).
太字の単語は強く言い、★のところで一拍おいて声に出してパートナーに聞こえる声で読んでみましょう。

1. Can you guess how many **brothers** and **sisters** I have? ★ **Seven!**
2. I went to the **best** restaurant in my town. ★ The **Big Cow Steak House**.
3. My teacher eats the **same** breakfast **every day**. ★ **Toast** and **milk**.

## Rehearsal

1 Before your rehearsal, check the boxes to make sure you are ready.
リハーサル前に準備ができているか確認して□に✓を付けましょう。

### Rehearsal Checklist

**Preparation** 準備

- □ ① Use large, clear photos for the slides. 大きくて見やすい写真を使う。
- □ ② Memorize your script. スクリプトを暗記する。
- □ ③ Have all computer devices ready.
  コンピューターやプロジェクター等の用意をする。

**Delivery** 発表

- □ ④ Stand with a good posture and smile. 正しい姿勢で立ち、笑顔を作る。
- □ ⑤ Make eye contact. アイコンタクトをとる。
- □ ⑥ Use a clear voice. 聞きやすい大きさの声で話す。

2 Rehearse your presentation. リハーサルをしましょう。

3 Write the numbers of the points you need to work on.
改善したいポイントの番号を上から選んで書きましょう。

| | Rehearsal | Number | Notes |
|---|---|---|---|
| 1 | Date / / | | |
| 2 | Date / / | | |
| 3 | Date / / | | |

# Evaluate it!

## Evaluation

Think back to your presentation and make your notes.
Ask your teacher and audience for comments.
自分のプレゼンを振り返って、自分の評価や、先生や聞き手の感想を書いておきましょう。

プレゼンはうまくいったかな？
他の人の意見も大切に聞こう。

## Self-evaluation

◎=Very good　○=Good　△=Try harder

| | | ◎/○/△ | Notes |
|---|---|---|---|
| 1 | Memorization<br>暗記 | | |
| 2 | Posture, smile, and eye contact<br>姿勢、笑顔とアイコンタクト | | |
| 3 | Clear voice<br>(Stresses and pauses)<br>聞きやすい大きさの声<br>(強弱と間の取り方) | | |
| 4 | Content<br>内容 | | |

## Teacher's and audience's comments

## Audience's Comments

1 Say the comments with the samples.
映像と一緒にコメントを言ってみましょう。

2 Use the sample comments and say your own.
例を参考に下線の単語を置きかえてコメントしましょう。

❶ I liked the picture of Umikaze Park.
うみかぜ公園の写真が好きでした。

❷ I liked the opening part of your presentation.
プレゼンの出だしが好きでした。

❸ I'd like to visit Yokosuka one day.
私もいつか横須賀に行ってみたいです。

❹ I think the place you live is very nice.
あなたの住んでいる所はとても素敵だと思います。

❺ I learned something new from your presentation.
あなたのプレゼンから新しいことを学びました。

❻ I learned many things about Yokosuka kaigun curry.
よこすか海軍カレーについてたくさんのことを学びました。

プレゼンを見ながらコメントを言うためのメモを取ろう。

Notes

---

---

---

---

---

---

# Presentation 2 What I Love

Step
1
2
3
4
5
Watch it!

## Sample Presentation

Watch the sample presentation.
サンプルプレゼンを見ましょう。

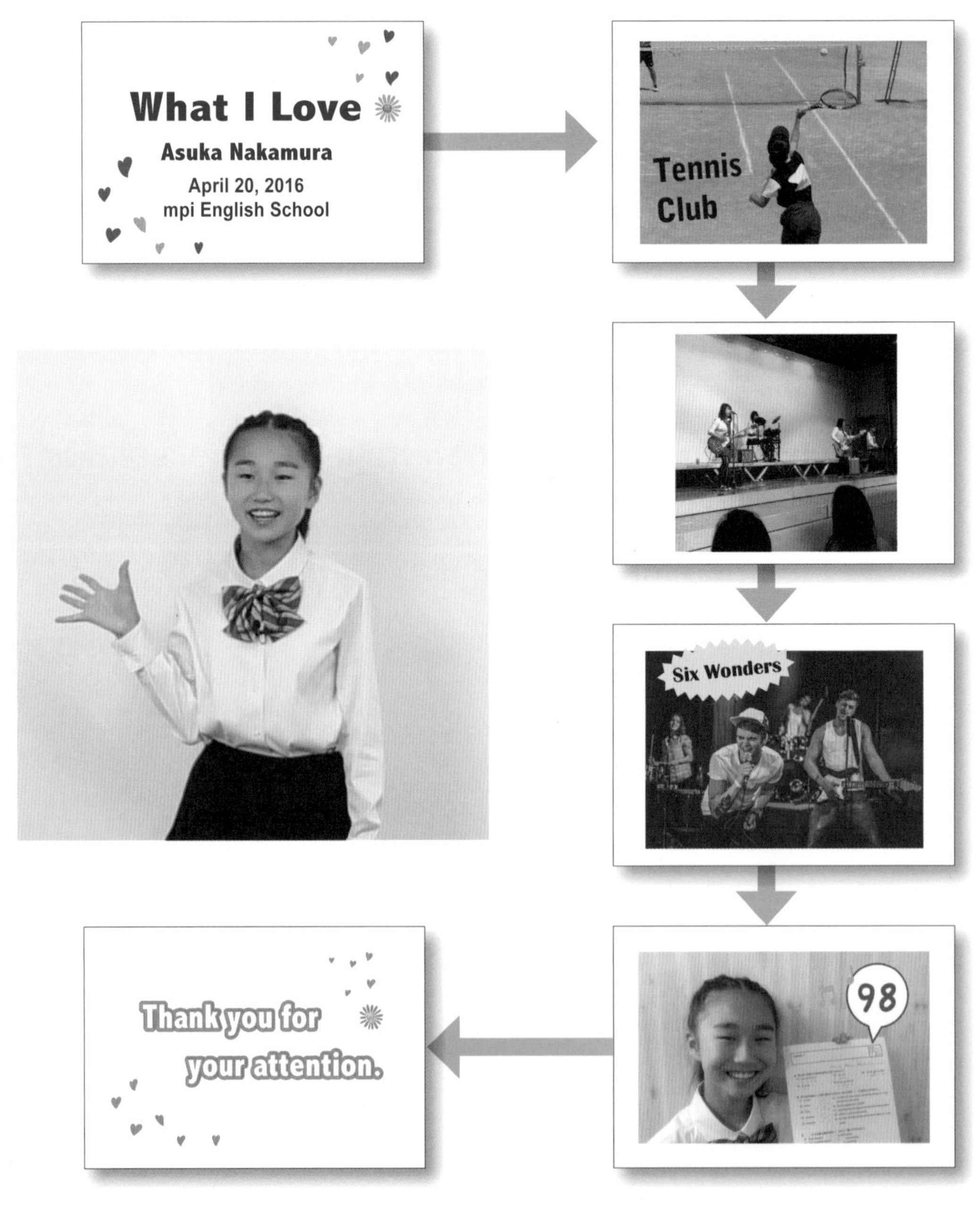

What I Love
Asuka Nakamura
April 20, 2016
mpi English School
Tennis Club
Six Wonders
98
Thank you for your attention.

## Activities

Watch the sample presentation again carefully.
Do the activities.

サンプルプレゼンを何回も見てアクティビティーをしましょう。

**1.** Which points were good? Circle your answers.

どのポイントが良かったですか？○を付けましょう。

| Posture | Smile | Eye contact | Clear voice | Stresses and pauses | Body movements |
|---|---|---|---|---|---|
| 姿勢 | 笑顔 | アイコンタクト | 聞きやすい声 | 強弱と間の取り方 | ジェスチャーなど |

**2.** What club does the presenter belong to?

プレゼンターは何部に所属していますか？

**She belongs to the** ______________________________ .

**3.** How often does the presenter practice the guitar?

プレゼンターはどのくらいの頻度でギターの練習をしていますか？

**She practices the guitar** ______________________________ .

**4.** Why does the presenter like Six Wonders' songs?

なぜプレゼンターは、Six Wonders の歌が好きなのですか？

**She likes their songs because** ______________________________ .

**5.** Who's your favorite musician or band?

あなたの好きなバンドまたは歌手は誰ですか？

**My favorite** ______________________________ .

## Step 1 2 3 4 5 Write it!

間をおいたり、ゆっくり言っているところに気を付けよう！

### Sample Script

Read along with the sample reading three times.
映像を見ながらスクリプトを３回読みましょう。

**Title** **What I Love**

**Opening** (Introduction)

1. Hi, I'm Asuka Nakamura.
2. I'm the captain of my school tennis club.
3. After tennis club practice, I'm always tired and sleepy.
4. That's why I often forget to do my homework. I'm sorry, teachers! ❶
5. I love tennis, but it's not what I love most.
6. What I love most is music.
7. I love both playing and listening to music.

**Body 1**

8. This is a photo of me playing the guitar in a band.
9. We won the best performance award at this year's school festival.
10. Isn't it exciting?
11. I enjoy playing the guitar, because it makes me feel better when I'm upset. ❷
12. I practice the guitar every day, so that our band can win again.
13. Now, please look at this picture.
14. This is my favorite band called Six Wonders, and they are popular for the song "Let me go." ❷
15. I love their music, because it makes me positive and happy. ❸

**Body 2**

16. I even keep music on while I study.
17. My mother and I always argue about it, because she doesn't believe I'm studying.
18. But I always get good grades in my English exams.
19. If you've never tried listening to music while studying, you may want to try it once.

**Closing** (Conclusion)

20. Music is the most important thing in my life, and I want to keep playing and listening to it for the rest of my life.
21. I hope you have something you love to do, like me.
22. Thank you for your attention.

## Key Sentences

Choose the key sentences for your own script.
自分のスクリプト用にキーセンテンスを選びましょう。

### ❶ Attention grabber
最初に印象付ける方法

☐ 1. Say something funny.（おもしろい事を言う）

☐ 2. Exaggerate things.（大げさに言う）

☐ 3. Use big body movements.（大きな身振りを付けて言う）

☐ 4. ______________________________

思いつく
自分のプレゼンの
キーワードを
書いてみよう。

### ❷ Introducing your favorite
好きな事を紹介する表現

☐ 1. I enjoy ____________ .

☐ 2. This is my favorite ____________ .

☐ 3. I really like ____________ .

☐ 4. I always ____________ .

☐ 5. ______________________________

### ❸ Giving reasons
理由を説明する表現

☐ 1. I love ____________, because it makes me ____________ .

☐ 2. I love it! Why? Because ____________ .

☐ 3. It's my favorite, because ____________ .

☐ 4. Let me tell you why I ____________ .

☐ 5. ______________________________

# Design it!

## My Presentation

1 Write the title and the closing expression on the slides.
①にタイトル、⑥に終わりの言葉を書きましょう。

2 Design your slides.
スライドのイメージを描きましょう。

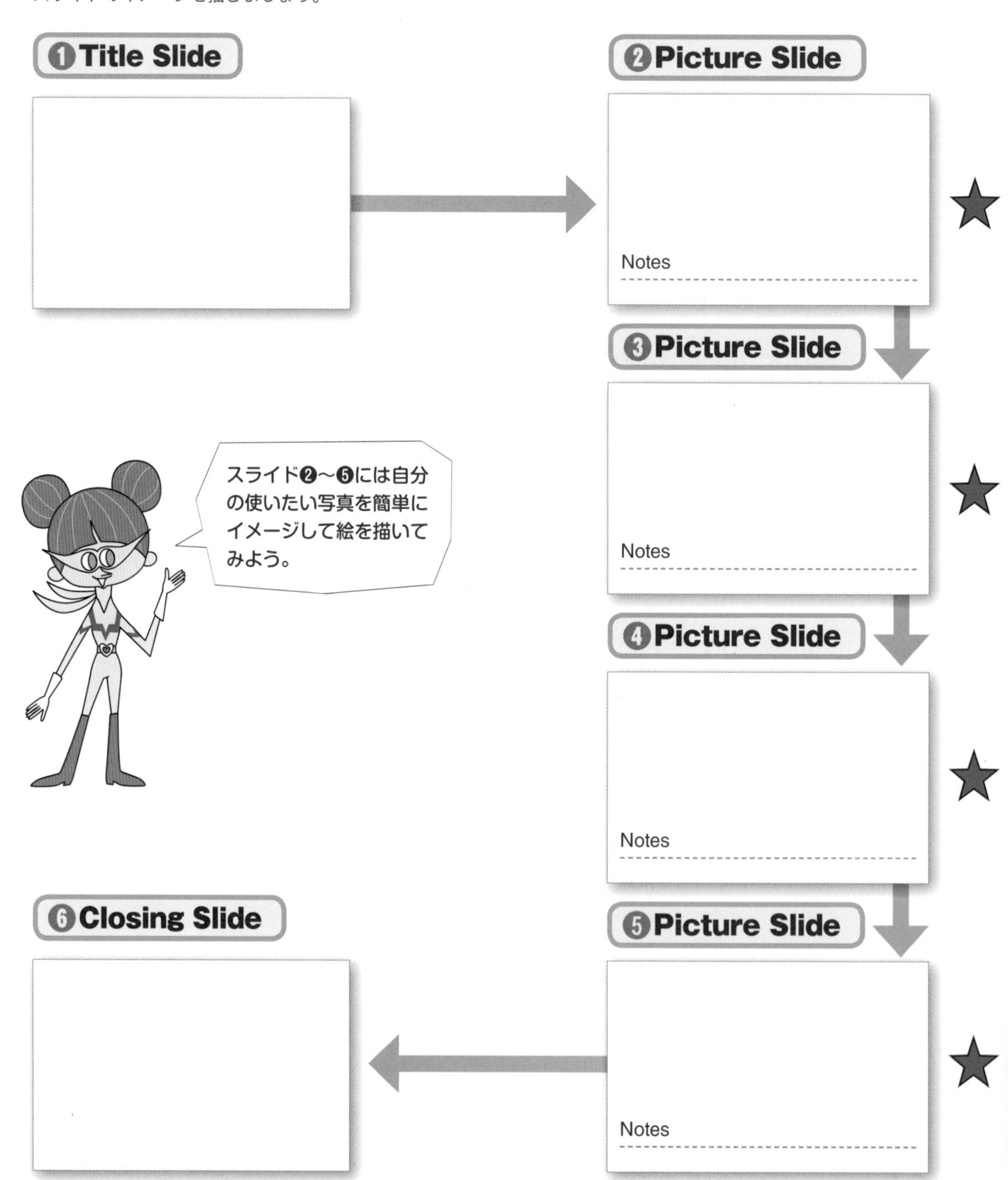

ステップ2で作った自分の
スクリプトを書こう。

3 Write your final script.
スクリプトを清書しましょう。

4 Connect the slides (★) and the script lines.
スライド（★）とそれを見せる時の文をつなぎましょう。

例：★⟶ 4.

**Title**

Opening (Introduction)

1. ____
2. ____
3. ____
4. ____
5. ____

Body 1

6. ____
7. ____
8. ____
9. ____
10. ____
11. ____

Body 2

12. ____
13. ____
14. ____
15. ____
16. ____
17. ____
18. ____
19. ____

Closing (Conclusion)

20. ____
21. ____
22. ____

# Present it!

## My Presentation

1 Write keywords or draw icons to help you memorize your script.
スクリプトを覚えるためにキーワードかアイコンを描きましょう。

2 Say your script by looking at the keywords and icons.
キーワードとアイコンを見ながらスクリプトを言ってみましょう。

1. ______________________
2. ______________________
3. ______________________
4. ______________________
5. ______________________
6. ______________________
7. ______________________
8. ______________________
9. ______________________
10. ______________________
11. ______________________
12. ______________________
13. ______________________
14. ______________________
15. ______________________
16. ______________________
17. ______________________
18. ______________________
19. ______________________
20. ______________________
21. ______________________
22. ______________________

↑山折り

## Presentation Skills Practice

**Body Movements** 体で表現する

Stand in pairs and face each other. Take turns to check the body movements are big and clear enough, while expressing the following:
ペアになり、向かい合って立ちましょう。下の3つを体で表現してみましょう。

1. Sequences: first / second / third

2. Adjectives: big / small, long / short, fast / slow, good / bad

3. Feelings: happy / tired / excited / love

## Rehearsal

1 Before your rehearsal, check the boxes to make sure you are ready.
リハーサル前に準備ができているか確認して□に✓を付けましょう。

### Rehearsal Checklist

**Preparation** 準備

- □ ① Use large, clear photos for the slides. 大きくて見やすい写真を使う。
- □ ② Memorize your script. スクリプトを暗記する。
- □ ③ Have all computer devices ready.
  コンピューターやプロジェクター等の用意をする。

**Delivery** 発表

- □ ④ Stand with a good posture and smile. 正しい姿勢で立ち、笑顔を作る。
- □ ⑤ Make eye contact. アイコンタクトをとる。
- □ ⑥ Use a clear voice. 聞きやすい大きさの声で話す。
- □ ⑦ Use body movements. 体で表現する。

2 Rehearse your presentation. リハーサルをしましょう。

3 Write the numbers of the points you need to work on.
改善したいポイントの番号を上から選んで書きましょう。

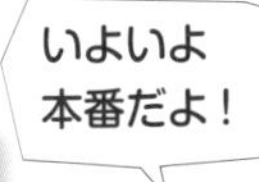


| | Rehearsal | Number | Notes |
|---|---|---|---|
| 1 | Date<br>/ / | | |
| 2 | Date<br>/ / | | |
| 3 | Date<br>/ / | | |

# Step 1 2 3 4 5 Evaluate it!

**Evaluation**

Think back to your presentation and make your notes.
Ask your teacher and audience for comments.
自分のプレゼンを振り返って、自分の評価や、先生や聞き手の感想を書いておきましょう。

プレゼンはうまくいったかな？
他の人の意見も大切に聞こう。

| **Self-evaluation** | ◎=Very good ○=Good △=Try harder | | |
|---|---|---|---|
| 1 | Memorization<br>暗記 | ◎/○/△ | Notes |
| 2 | Posture, smile, and eye contact<br>姿勢、笑顔とアイコンタクト | ◎/○/△ | Notes |
| 3 | Clear voice<br>(Stresses and pauses)<br>聞きやすい大きさの声<br>（強弱と間の取り方） | ◎/○/△ | Notes |
| 4 | Body movements<br>体で表現する | ◎/○/△ | Notes |
| 5 | Content<br>内容 | ◎/○/△ | Notes |

## Teacher's and audience's comments

# Presentation 2 What I Love

## Audience's Comments

1 Say the comments with the samples.
映像と一緒にコメントを言ってみましょう。

2 Use the sample comments and say your own.
例を参考に下線の単語を置きかえてコメントしましょう。

❶ I think Six Wonders is great too.
私も Six Wonders はすごいと思います。

❷ I also like music, because it's exciting.
わくわくするので、私も音楽が好きです。

❸ It was good to find out you won the best performance award.
あなたがベストパフォーマンス賞を取った事を知ることができて良かったです。

❹ It's the first time I've heard about Six Wonders.
Six Wonders について聞くのは初めてでした。

❺ I'd like to play the guitar too.
私もギターを弾いてみたいです。

❻ I feel like listening to music now.
私も今、音楽を聴きたい気分になりました。

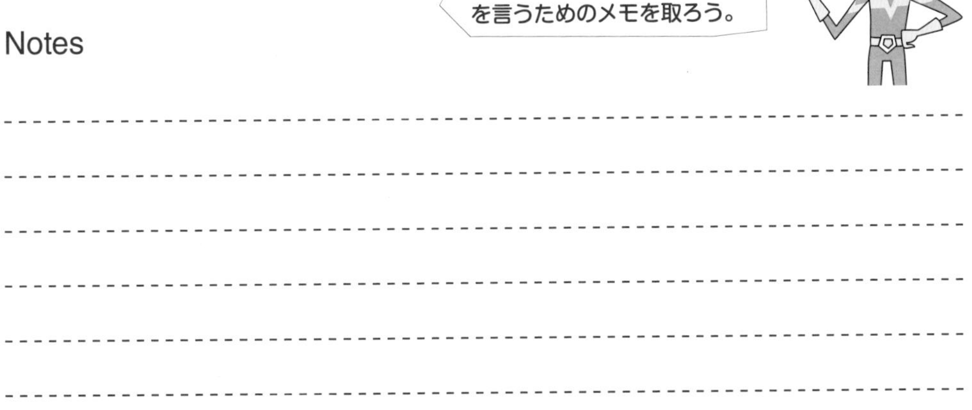

プレゼンを見ながらコメント
を言うためのメモを取ろう。
Notes

# Presentation 3 Historical Figures

## Step 1 2 3 4 5 Watch it!

### Sample Presentation

Watch the sample presentation.
サンプルプレゼンを見ましょう。

## Activities

Watch the sample presentation again carefully.
Do the activities.
サンプルプレゼンを何回も見てアクティビティーをしましょう。

**1.** Which points were good? Circle your answers.
どのポイントが良かったですか？○を付けましょう。

| | | | |
|---|---|---|---|
| **Posture** 姿勢 | **Smile** 笑顔 | **Eye contact** アイコンタクト | **Clear voice** 聞きやすい声 |
| **Stresses and pauses** 強弱と間の取り方 | **Body movements** ジェスチャーなど | **Confidence** 自信ある態度 | |

**2.** The presenter uses his mobile phone as a watch, a dictionary, and for what else?
プレゼンターは時計、辞書の他に何として携帯電話を使いますか？

**He uses it as a watch, a dictionary, and for** ______________________ .

**3.** Where was Alexander Graham Bell born?
アレクサンダー・グラハム・ベルは、どこで生まれましたか？

**He was born in** ______________________________________ .

**4.** What did Alexander Graham Bell invent?
アレクサンダー・グラハム・ベルは何を発明しましたか？

**He invented** ________________________________________ .

**5.** Do you have a mobile phone? If so, when do you use it?
あなたは携帯電話を持っていますか？持っているとしたらいつ使いますか？

**I** ______________________________________________ .

# Step 1 2 3 4 5 Write it!

間をおいたり、ゆっくり言っているところに気を付けよう！

## Sample Script

Read along with the sample reading three times.
映像を見ながらスクリプトを３回読みましょう。

**Title** **A Person Who Changed Our World**

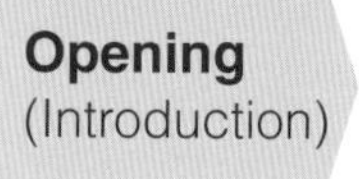

**Opening** (Introduction)

1. Hi, my name is Jiro Miyazaki.
2. I'm from mpi English School.
3. I use my mobile phone as a watch, a dictionary, and of course for games.
4. My mother says my mobile phone is my best friend. ❶
5. Well, I agree.
6. Today, I'd like to introduce a famous person from world history. ❷

**Body 1**

7. This is Alexander Graham Bell, and he invented the first telephone. ❸
8. He was born in Edinburgh, Scotland in 1847.
9. His mother and wife both had hearing problems.
10. His father and grandfather were both teachers for the hearing impaired.
11. In order to help them, Bell wanted to invent something useful for people.
12. I believe his family background greatly influenced his invention.

**Body 2**

13. Please take a look at this picture. Do you know what this is?
14. This is the first drawing of the telephone that Bell invented.
15. I respect him, because he didn't give up and invented something new and super convenient for our everyday lives. ❷
16. The other day, I had a fight with my best friend, Tsubasa, at school.
17. We had a fight because we misunderstood each other.
18. When I got home, I felt really bad, so I called him on the phone and said sorry.
19. If Bell hadn't invented the telephone, I might not be friends with Tsubasa anymore.
20. We should all thank the genius Bell for inventing such a brilliant tool.

**Closing** (Conclusion)

21. I think Alexander Graham Bell changed our world the most of anyone in the last two hundred years.
22. Thank you, Mr. Bell, and thank you for listening.

## Key Sentences

Choose the key sentences for your own script.
自分のスクリプト用にキーセンテンスを選びましょう。

### ❶ Attention grabber
最初に印象付ける表現

Exaggerate things
**〈Examples〉**

- ☐ 1. My mother says my mobile phone is my best friend.
- ☐ 2. I send more than one million text messages a day.
- ☐ 3. I use my mobile phone every single minute.
- ☐ 4. I can't live without my mobile phone.
- ☐ 5. ______________________________

思いつく
自分のプレゼンの
キーワードを
書いてみよう。

### ❷ Introducing a person / group
人やグループを紹介する表現

- ☐ 1. I'd like to introduce __________ .
- ☐ 2. I respect _____ because __________ .
- ☐ 3. I believe that he / she is the best _________ .
- ☐ 4. I look up to him / her very much because _____ .
- ☐ 5. I want to be like ____________ someday.
- ☐ 6. ______________________________

### ❸ Introducing what he / she did
功績を説明する表現

- ☐ 1. He / She invented __________ .
- ☐ 2. He / She is the first person who __________ .
- ☐ 3. He / She changed __________ .
- ☐ 4. He / She created __________ .
- ☐ 5. He / She produced __________ .
- ☐ 6. ______________________________

## My Presentation

1 Write the title and the closing expression on the slides.
①にタイトル、⑥に終わりの言葉を書きましょう。

2 Design your slides.
スライドのイメージを描きましょう。

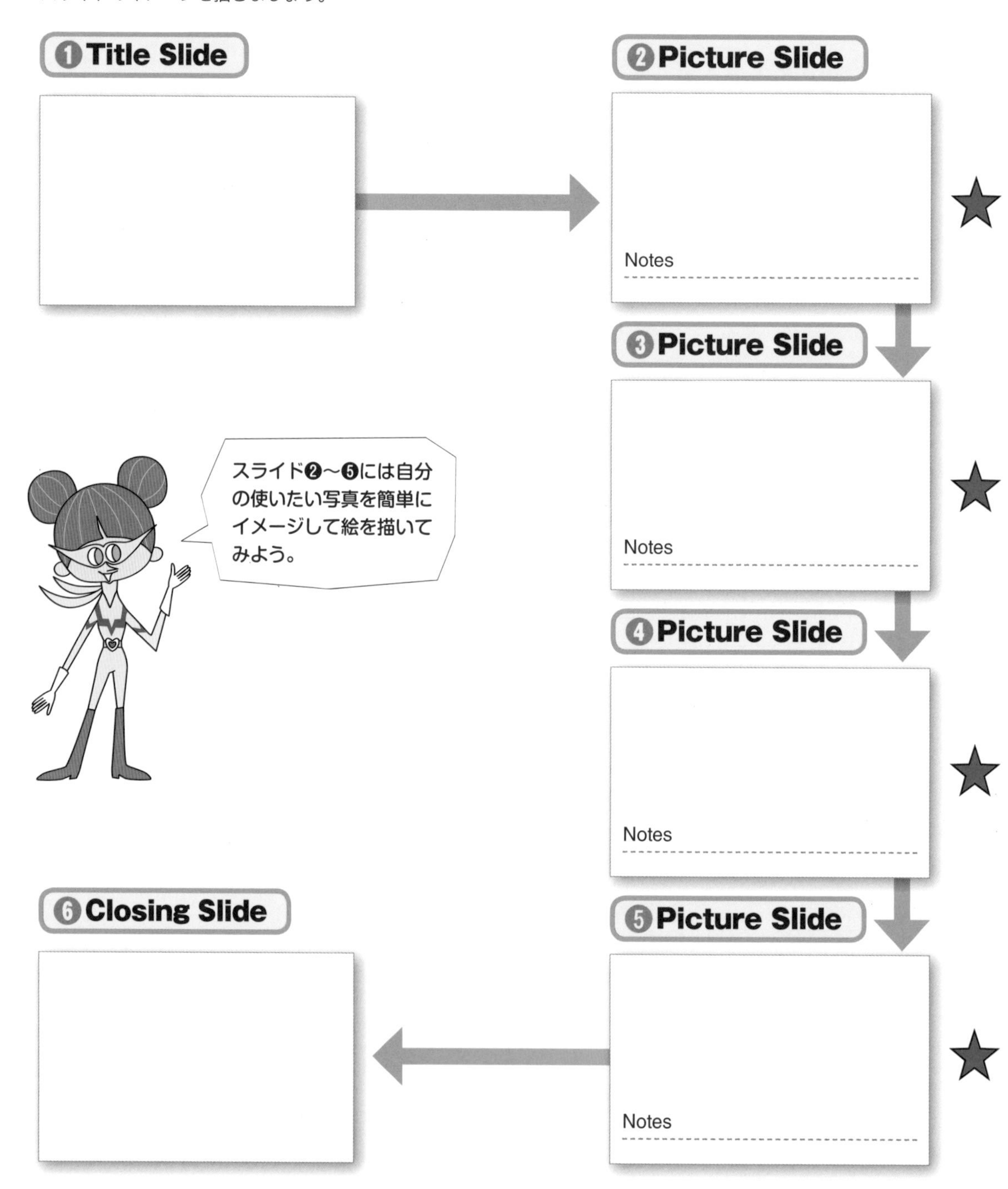

ステップ2で作った自分の
スクリプトを書こう。

3 Write your final script.
スクリプトを清書しましょう。

4 Connect the slides (★) and the script lines.
スライド（★）とそれを見せる時の文をつなぎましょう。

例：★──→ 4.

## Title

Opening (Introduction)

1. ____________________
2. ____________________
3. ____________________
4. ____________________

Body 1

5. ____________________
6. ____________________
7. ____________________
8. ____________________
9. ____________________
10. ____________________
11. ____________________

Body 2

12. ____________________
13. ____________________
14. ____________________
15. ____________________
16. ____________________
17. ____________________
18. ____________________
19. ____________________

Closing (Conclusion)

20. ____________________
21. ____________________
22. ____________________

Step 1 2 3 4 5

# Present it!

## My Presentation

1 Write keywords or draw icons to help you memorize your script.
スクリプトを覚えるためにキーワードかアイコンを描きましょう。

2 Say your script by looking at the keywords and icons.
キーワードとアイコンを見ながらスクリプトを言ってみましょう。

1. ____________________
2. ____________________
3. ____________________
4. ____________________
5. ____________________
6. ____________________
7. ____________________
8. ____________________
9. ____________________
10. ____________________
11. ____________________
12. ____________________
13. ____________________
14. ____________________
15. ____________________
16. ____________________
17. ____________________
18. ____________________
19. ____________________
20. ____________________
21. ____________________
22. ____________________

↑山折り

## Presentation Skills Practice

**Be Confident** 自信を持つ

Have a routine before you make a presentation to relax and become more confident.
リラックスし、自信を持つためにルーティンを決めましょう。

**〈Examples〉**

1. Rotate your head, hands, and shoulders.
   頭や手や肩を回しましょう。
2. Put your hands on your hips.
   腰に手を当てましょう。

3. Close your eyes for five seconds.
   5秒間目を閉じましょう。
4. Take a deep breath.
   深呼吸をしましょう。

5. Say "I can do it!" to yourself.
   「できるぞ！」と自分に言いましょう。

## Rehearsal

1 Before your rehearsal, check the boxes to make sure you are ready.
リハーサル前に準備ができているか確認して□に✓を付けましょう。

### Rehearsal Checklist

**Preparation** 準備

- □ ① Use large, clear photos for the slides. 大きくて見やすい写真を使う。
- □ ② Memorize your script. スクリプトを暗記する。
- □ ③ Have all computer devices ready.
  コンピューターやプロジェクター等の用意をする。

**Delivery** 発表

- □ ④ Stand with a good posture and smile. 正しい姿勢で立ち、笑顔を作る。
- □ ⑤ Make eye contact. アイコンタクトをとる。
- □ ⑥ Use a clear voice. 聞きやすい大きさの声で話す。
- □ ⑦ Use body movements. 体で表現する。
- □ ⑧ Be confident. 自信を持つ。

2 Rehearse your presentation. リハーサルをしましょう。

3 Write the numbers of the points you need to work on.
改善したいポイントの番号を上から選んで書きましょう。

| | Rehearsal | Number | Notes |
|---|---|---|---|
| 1 | Date / / | | |
| 2 | Date / / | | |
| 3 | Date / / | | |

# Step 1 2 3 4 5 Evaluate it!

## Evaluation

Think back to your presentation and make your notes.
Ask your teacher and audience for comments.

自分のプレゼンを振り返って、自分の評価や、先生や聞き手の感想を書いておきましょう。

プレゼンはうまくいったかな？
他の人の意見も大切に聞こう。

**Self-evaluation** ◎=Very good ○=Good △=Try harder

| | | ◎/○/△ | Notes |
|---|---|---|---|
| 1 | Memorization<br>暗記 | | |
| 2 | Posture, smile, and eye contact<br>姿勢、笑顔とアイコンタクト | | |
| 3 | Clear voice<br>(Stresses and pauses)<br>聞きやすい大きさの声<br>（強弱と間の取り方） | | |
| 4 | Body movements<br>体で表現する | | |
| 5 | Confidence<br>自信を持つ | | |
| 6 | Content<br>内容 | | |

## Teacher's and audience's comments

## Audience's Comments

1 Say the comments with the samples.
映像と一緒にコメントを言ってみましょう。

2 Use the sample comments and say your own.
例を参考に下線の単語を置きかえてコメントしましょう。

❶ I really enjoyed the opening part of your presentation, because your joke was funny.
ジョークが面白かったので、プレゼンの出だしが楽しかったです。

❷ It was good to know about Bell's invention, because I use my phone every day too.
私も毎日電話を使うので、ベルの発明について知ることができて良かったです。

❸ It was very interesting, because it was the first time I'd heard about Bell's family.
ベルの家族について聞くのは初めてだったので、興味深かったです。

❹ I think Bell is great too. I want to find out more about his challenges.
私もベルはすごいと思います。彼の挑戦についてもっと知りたいです。

❺ I also like Bell, because I think the telephone is a great tool.
電話は優れた機器だと思うので、私もベルが好きです。

❻ I really liked your presentation, because I had a similar experience with my friend too.
私も同じような経験を友達としたので、あなたのプレゼンテーションを気に入りました。

プレゼンを見ながらコメントを言うためのメモを取ろう。

Notes

---

---

---

# Presentation 4 Make Your Own

## Plan it!

### Presentation Topic

Decide on your topic for the presentation.
紹介したいトピックを決めましょう。

1 Think about people, places or things that are important to you.
Write them down. Circle one you want to introduce the most.
あなたにとって大切な事、人、場所を考えて書き出してみましょう。そして、一番紹介したいと思うものに○を付けましょう。

例 My favorite place / Who I look up to / books / movies / music / sport
大好きな場所　あこがれの人　本　映画　音楽　スポーツ

2 Write down everything you know about it.
○を付けたものに関して知っていることを全部書きだしてみましょう。

3 Circle two things you feel strongly about.
特に自分の思いが強いものを２つ○で囲みましょう。

4 Write what you think and feel about each of them. Answer each question below.

3で選んだ２つについてあなたが考えたり感じたりしていることは何ですか。下の質問に答えましょう。

トピックに関連して選んだ２つのキーワードについてそれぞれ考えてみよう。


① Why is it important to you?

1. Because ______________________________ .

2. Because ______________________________ .

② How do you feel about it?

1. ______________________________ .

2. ______________________________ .

③ What do you think about it?

1. I think ______________________________ .

2. I think ______________________________ .

④ What are its good points?

1. ______________________________ .

2. ______________________________ .

## Draft Script

Write your draft script based on your keywords and phrases.
キーワードやキーフレーズをまとめてスクリプトの下書きをしましょう。

**Title**

**Opening** (Introduction)

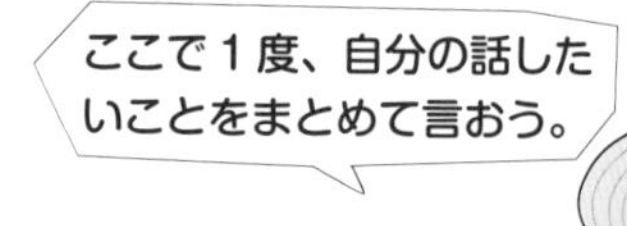

なぜ、このトピックにしたのか具体例を出して言おう。

## Body 2

さらにもう１つの理由を
具体的に言おう。

## Closing (Conclusion)

最後に言いたかったこと、伝えたかった
ことをまとめてもう一度言おう。

# Design it!

## My Presentation

1 Write the title and the closing expression on the slides.
①にタイトル、⑥に終わりの言葉を書きましょう。

2 Design your slides.
スライドのイメージを描きましょう。

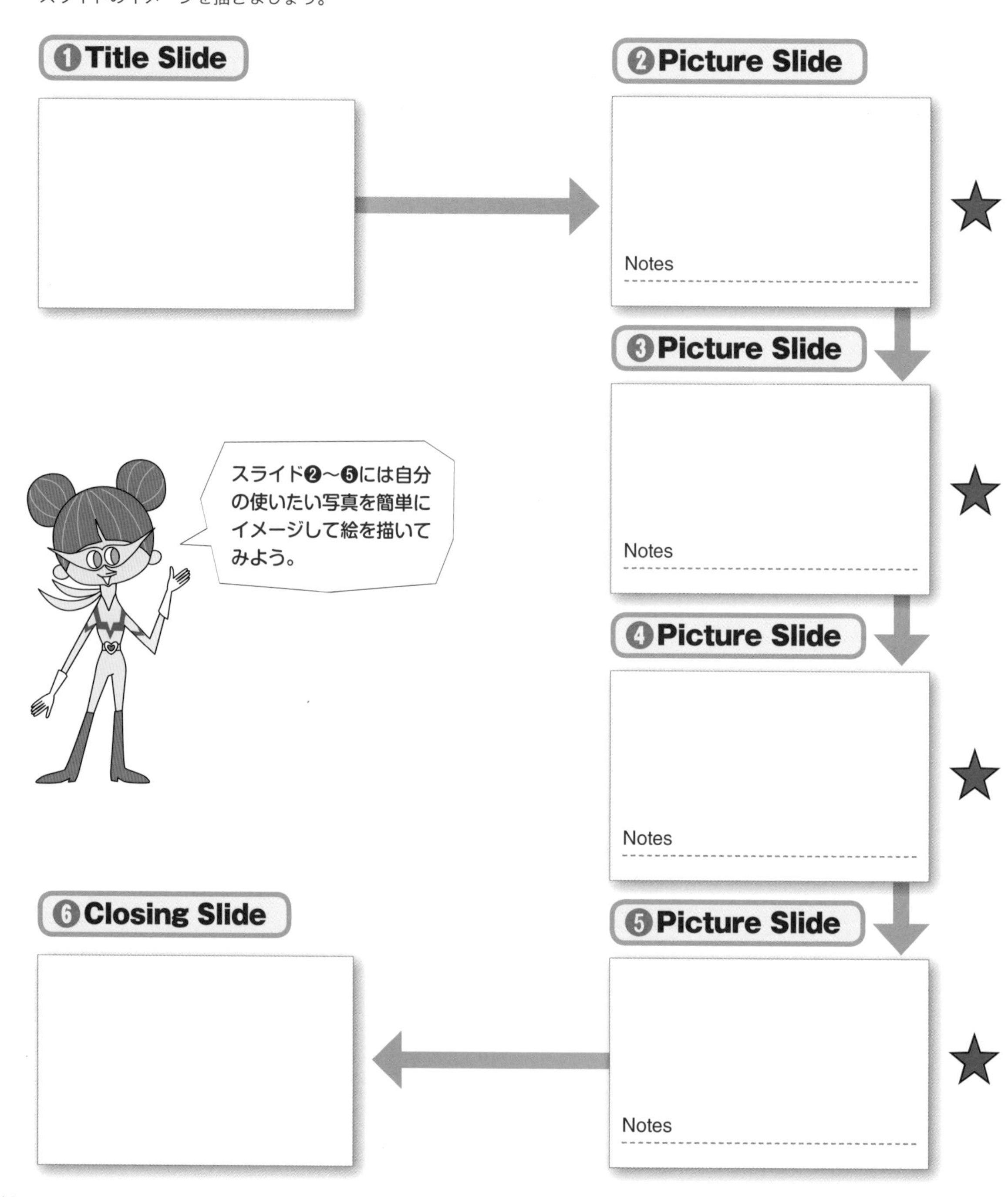

3 Write your final script.
スクリプトを清書しましょう。

4 Connect the slides (★) and the script lines.
スライド（★）とそれを見せる時の文をつなぎましょう。

例：★──→ 4.

ステップ2で作った自分のスクリプトを書こう。

**Title**

Opening (Introduction)

1. ______
2. ______
3. ______
4. ______
5. ______

Body 1

6. ______
7. ______
8. ______
9. ______
10. ______
11. ______
12. ______

Body 2

13. ______
14. ______
15. ______
16. ______
17. ______
18. ______
19. ______
20. ______

Closing (Conclusion)

21. ______
22. ______
23. ______

# Step 1 2 3 4 5 Present it!

## My Presentation

1 Write keywords or draw icons to help you memorize your script.
スクリプトを覚えるためにキーワードかアイコンを描きましょう。

2 Say your script by looking at the keywords and icons.
キーワードとアイコンを見ながらスクリプトを言ってみましょう。

1. ______
2. ______
3. ______
4. ______
5. ______
6. ______
7. ______
8. ______
9. ______
10. ______
11. ______
12. ______
13. ______
14. ______
15. ______
16. ______
17. ______
18. ______
19. ______
20. ______
21. ______
22. ______
23. ______

山折り

## Presentation Skills Practice

**Review** もう一度練習しましょう。

❶ Practice using a clear voice with stresses and pauses. (p.14)
強弱と間のとり方に気を付けながら、聞きやすい大きさの声で話す練習をしましょう。

❷ Practice using body movements. (p.24)
ジェスチャーをする練習をしましょう。

❸ Practice your routine to relax and be confident. (p.34)
リラックスし、自信を持つためにルーティンを練習しましょう。

## Rehearsal

1 Before your rehearsal, check the boxes to make sure you are ready.
リハーサル前に準備ができているか確認して□に✓を付けましょう。

### Rehearsal Checklist

**Preparation** 準備

- □ ① Use large, clear photos for the slides. 大きくて見やすい写真を使う。
- □ ② Memorize your script. スクリプトを暗記する。
- □ ③ Have all computer devices ready.
  コンピューターやプロジェクター等の用意をする。

**Delivery** 発表

- □ ④ Stand with a good posture and smile. 正しい姿勢で立ち、笑顔を作る。
- □ ⑤ Make eye contact. アイコンタクトをとる。
- □ ⑥ Use a clear voice. 聞きやすい大きさの声で話す。
- □ ⑦ Use body movements. 体で表現する。
- □ ⑧ Be confident. 自信を持つ。

2 Rehearse your presentation. リハーサルをしましょう。

3 Write the numbers of the points you need to work on.
改善したいポイントの番号を上から選んで書きましょう。

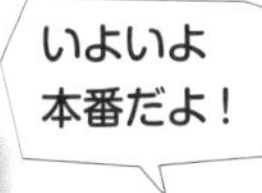


| | Rehearsal | Number | Notes |
|---|---|---|---|
| 1 | Date / / | | |
| 2 | Date / / | | |
| 3 | Date / / | | |

# Step 1 2 3 4 5 Evaluate it!

## Evaluation

Think back to your presentation and make your notes.
Ask your teacher and audience for comments.
自分のプレゼンを振り返って、自分の評価や、先生や聞き手の感想を書いておきましょう。

プレゼンはうまくいったかな？
他の人の意見も大切に聞こう。

| | Self-evaluation | ◎=Very good ○=Good △=Try harder | |
|---|---|---|---|
| 1 | Memorization<br>暗記 | ◎/○/△ | Notes |
| 2 | Posture, smile, and eye contact<br>姿勢、笑顔とアイコンタクト | ◎/○/△ | Notes |
| 3 | Clear voice<br>(Stresses and pauses)<br>聞きやすい大きさの声<br>(強弱と間の取り方) | ◎/○/△ | Notes |
| 4 | Body movements<br>体で表現する | ◎/○/△ | Notes |
| 5 | Confidence<br>自信を持つ | ◎/○/△ | Notes |
| 6 | Content<br>内容 | ◎/○/△ | Notes |

## Teacher's and audience's comments

Keep a record of the presentations you watched.

友達のプレゼンを見たら記録に残しておきましょう。

例

| No: 1 | Date: 9/10 | Presenter: Asuka | Topic: What I love | | | |
|---|---|---|---|---|---|---|
| Evaluation: | Memorization | ○ | Posture, smile, and eye contact | ◎ | Clear voice | ◎ |
| | Body movements | ◎ | Confidence | ◎ | Content | ○ |
| Note: six wonders | | | | | | |

| No: | Date: | Presenter: | Topic: | | | |
|---|---|---|---|---|---|---|
| Evaluation: | Memorization | | Posture, smile, and eye contact | | Clear voice | |
| | Body movements | | Confidence | | Content | |
| Note: | | | | | | |

| No: | Date: | Presenter: | Topic: | | | |
|---|---|---|---|---|---|---|
| Evaluation: | Memorization | | Posture, smile, and eye contact | | Clear voice | |
| | Body movements | | Confidence | | Content | |
| Note: | | | | | | |

| No: | Date: | Presenter: | Topic: | | | |
|---|---|---|---|---|---|---|
| Evaluation: | Memorization | | Posture, smile, and eye contact | | Clear voice | |
| | Body movements | | Confidence | | Content | |
| Note: | | | | | | |

| No: | Date: | Presenter: | Topic: | | | |
|---|---|---|---|---|---|---|
| Evaluation: | Memorization | | Posture, smile, and eye contact | | Clear voice | |
| | Body movements | | Confidence | | Content | |
| Note: | | | | | | |

質問力を上げよう！

# Poster Session・Basic

プレゼンで作った
スライドを使って、
ポスターセッションを
してみよう！

## Poster Session とは？

一般的なポスターセッションでは、自分の研究した事/調べた事をビジュアルにまとめたポスターを壁やホワイトボードに貼り出し、ポスターを見に来た人に研究した事/調べた事を説明したり、意見交換をします。

## この本のPoster Session では

- 何度も質問に答えることで、段々と自信がつきます。
- アイコントクトができるようになります。
- 大きな声で発表するための練習ができます。

### 1 Make a poster using your slides.

作ったスライドを使ってポスターを作ります。

名前とタイトルは必ず入れ、
その他は自由にデザインしよう！

Sample poster

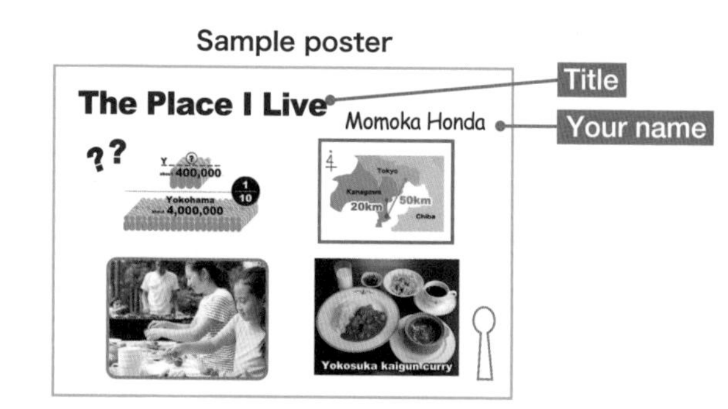


### 2 Follow the steps for a successful poster session.

以下のようなパターンで会話を進めましょう。

<自己紹介をしましょう>

**Audience**
Asks the questions.

**Presenter**
Answers the questions.

**❶ Introduce yourself.** (Audience)
Hi, my name is ______.

**❶ Introduce yourself.** (Presenter)
Hi, my name is ______.

<どんなポスターかを聞いてみましょう>

**❷ Start off by asking about the title of the poster.**
So, your poster is about Japanese food?

**❷ Answer the question.**
Yes, it is.

<ポスターの写真について聞いてみましょう>

**❸ Ask a question.** Q

**❹ Make a comment.** C

**❸ Answer the question.** A

写真や絵の数だけ
このやり取りを
してみよう！

<お礼を言いましょう>

**❺ Say something nice at the end.**
Thank you. That was very interesting.

**❹ Say "Thank you."**
Thank you.

## 3 Make a pair. Write your questions about your partner's poster.

ペアになってお互いのポスターについて質問を考えて書きましょう。

Example What's this number?

Example Who are they?

The Place I Live

Momoka Honda

Example How long does it take to get to Tokyo?

Example Do you like curry and rice?

| Where どこ | What 何 | Which どっち | Who だれ | When いつ | How どのようにして | Is / Are ～ですか | Do / Does ～ですか |
|---|---|---|---|---|---|---|---|

○

○

○

○

○

○

○

○

○

## 4 Hold a poster session.

実際にポスターセッションをやってみましょう。

プレゼンターが外側、オーディエンスが内側で右の図にように円を作り、ペアになります。オーディエンスから質問を始めて会話をします。
時間（2分程度）が来たら、オーディエンスが隣のプレゼンターに移動して、同様に行います。クラスに合わせて制限時間を設定し、たくさんの人とやり取りできるとよいでしょう。

Presenter

Audience

一周したら、役割を交代しよう。

# サンプルスピーチのスクリプトのまとめ

## Presentation 1　The Place I Live

| | |
|---|---|
| 1. Hello, everyone. My name is Momoka Honda. | 1. 皆さん、こんにちは。私はホンダモモカです。 |
| 2. I'm from Minami School. | 2. ミナミ学校から来ました。 |
| 3. Please guess which city I live in. | 3. 私がどこの市に住んでいるか当ててみてください。 |
| 4. It's in Kanagawa Prefecture and starts with the letter "Y". | 4. 神奈川県にありＹで始まります。 |
| 5. The population is about four hundred thousand, which is only one-tenth of Yokohama City. | 5. 人口は約 40 万人で、横浜市のたった 10 分の 1 です。 |
| 6. Now do you know the answer? | 6. さぁ、答えがわかりましたか？ |
| 7. I live in Yokosuka City in Kanagawa Prefecture and it's a great place to live. | 7. 私は神奈川県の横須賀市に住んでいて、そこは住むのにとても良い場所です。 |
| 8. First, let's look at the map. | 8. 最初に、この地図をご覧ください。 |
| 9. Yokosuka is located fifty kilometers from Tokyo, and it takes about an hour and a half by train. | 9. 横須賀は東京から 50km の距離で、電車でだいたい 1 時間半かかります。 |
| 10. Tokyo Bay is to the east and Sagami Bay is to the west. | 10. 東に東京湾、西に相模湾があります。 |
| 11. There are historical areas, beautiful beaches, and many cozy parks in Yokosuka. | 11. 横須賀には歴史ある地域、美しい海岸や気持ちのいい公園があります。 |
| 12. This is a photo of my family. We are enjoying a barbeque in Umikaze Park. | 12. これは私たち家族の写真です。うみかぜ公園でバーベキューを楽しみました。 |
| 13. Umikaze Park is my favorite place in our city. | 13. うみかぜ公園は市内で私のお気に入りの場所です。 |
| 14. I think it's the best park in Yokosuka because people of all ages can enjoy many kinds of outdoor activities there. | 14. すべての年代の人がいろいろな野外活動を楽しめるので横須賀で一番の公園だと思います。 |
| 15. This is a picture of a famous food from Yokosuka. | 15. これは横須賀で有名な食べ物の写真です。 |
| 16. It's called Yokosuka kaigun curry. | 16. よこすか海軍カレーと呼ばれています。 |
| 17. Did you know that it was the first Japanese-style curry? | 17. これは最初の日本風カレーだと知っていましたか？ |
| 18. It first started in the Meiji era. | 18. 明治時代に最初に始まりました。 |
| 19. As you can see, it's made with beef and lots of vegetables. | 19. 見てわかるとおり、牛肉とたくさんの野菜が入っています。 |
| 20. It tastes great with a glass of milk. | 20. 牛乳と一緒に食べるととてもおいしいです。 |
| 21. I think Yokosuka is a fun place to live because it has lively parks and delicious food. | 21. 活気のある公園やおいしい食べ物があるので、横須賀は住むのに楽しい場所だと思います。 |
| 22. I hope you enjoyed my presentation and will visit Yokosuka someday. | 22. 私のプレゼンを楽しんでもらえ、いつか横須賀を訪ねてもらえたらいいなと思います。 |
| 23. Thank you for your attention. | 23. ご清聴ありがとうございました。 |

## Presentation 2 What I Love

| | |
|---|---|
| 1. Hi, I'm Asuka Nakamura. | 1. 私はナカムラアスカです。 |
| 2. I'm the captain of my school tennis club. | 2. 学校のテニス部の部長です。 |
| 3. After tennis club practice, I'm always tired and sleepy. | 3. 部活の後はいつも疲れていて眠いです。 |
| 4. That's why I often forget to do my homework. I'm sorry, teachers! | 4. なのでよく宿題を忘れてしまうのです。先生、ごめんなさい。 |
| 5. I love tennis, but it's not what I love most. | 5. 私はテニスが大好きですが、でもそれが一番好きなのではありません。 |
| 6. What I love most is music. | 6. 私が一番好きなのは音楽です。 |
| 7. I love both playing and listening to music. | 7. 音楽を演奏するのも聴くのも両方大好きです。 |
| 8. This is a photo of me playing the guitar in a band. | 8. これは私がバンドでギターを演奏している写真です。 |
| 9. We won the best performance award at this year's school festival. | 9. 今年の文化祭でベストパフォーマンス賞を取りました。 |
| 10. Isn't it exciting? | 10. すごくないですか？ |
| 11. I enjoy playing the guitar, because it makes me feel better when I'm upset. | 11. 落ち込んだ時に気分を良くしてくれるので、ギターを弾くのは楽しいです。 |
| 12. I practice the guitar every day, so that our band can win again. | 12. 私たちのバンドがまた賞を取れるように、私は毎日ギターの練習をしています。 |
| 13. Now, please look at this picture. | 13. 今度は、この写真をご覧ください。 |
| 14. This is my favorite band called Six Wonders, and they are popular for the song "Let me go". | 14. 私のお気に入りの Six Wonders と言うバンドで「Let me go」と言う曲で人気があります。 |
| 15. I love their music, because it makes me positive and happy. | 15. 彼らの音楽はポジティブに、そして幸せにしてくれるので、私は彼らの音楽が大好きです。 |
| 16. I even keep music on while I study. | 16. 私は勉強する時にも音楽をかけています。 |
| 17. My mother and I always argue about it, because she doesn't believe I'm studying. | 17. 私の母は私が勉強していると信じてくれないのでいつも言い争いになります。 |
| 18. But I always get good grades in my English exams. | 18. だけど英語の試験ではいつも良い点を取っています。 |
| 19. If you've never tried listening to music while studying, you may want to try it once. | 19. もし勉強をしながら音楽を聴いたことがないなら、一度試してみてください。 |
| 20. Music is the most important thing in my life, and I want to keep playing and listening to it for the rest of my life. | 20. 音楽は私の生活で一番重要です。これからもずっと音楽を演奏して、また聴いていきたいです。 |
| 21. I hope you have something you love to do, like me. | 21. あなたにも私のように何か大好きな物があるといいなと思います。 |
| 22. Thank you for your attention. | 22. ご清聴ありがとうございました。 |

## Presentation 3 Historical Figures

| | |
|---|---|
| 1. Hi, my name is Jiro Miyazaki. | 1. 私はミヤザキジロウです。 |
| 2. I'm from mpi English School. | 2. mpi イングリッシュスクールから来ました。 |
| 3. I use my mobile phone as a watch, a dictionary, and of course for games. | 3. 私は携帯電話を時計や辞書、もちろんゲーム機として使っています。 |
| 4. My mother says my mobile phone is my best friend. | 4. 私の母は、携帯電話は僕の親友だねと言います。 |
| 5. Well, I agree. | 5. まあ、同感です。 |
| 6. Today, I'd like to introduce a famous person from world history. | 6. 今日は世界の歴史から有名な人物を紹介したいと思います。 |
| 7. This is Alexander Graham Bell, and he invented the first telephone. | 7. これは、最初の電話を発明したアレクサンダー・グラハム・ベルです。 |
| 8. He was born in Edinburgh, Scotland in 1847. | 8. 彼は 1847 年にスコットランドのエジンバラで生まれました。 |
| 9. His mother and wife both had hearing problems. | 9. 彼のお母さんと妻は、聞くことが困難でした。 |
| 10. His father and grandfather were both teachers for the hearing impaired. | 10. 彼のお父さんとおじいさんは二人共、聞くことに障害のある人たちのための先生でした。 |
| 11. In order to help them, Bell wanted to invent something useful for people. | 11. ベルはそういう人を助けるために、人の役に立つ何かを発明したかったのです。 |
| 12. I believe his family background greatly influenced his invention. | 12. 私は家族環境が彼の発明に大きく影響を与えたと信じています。 |
| 13. Please take a look at this picture. Do you know what this is? | 13. この写真をご覧ください。何だかわかりますか？ |
| 14. This is the first drawing of the telephone that Bell invented. | 14. これは、ベルが発明した電話の最初の絵です。 |
| 15. I respect him, because he didn't give up and invented something new and super convenient for our everyday lives. | 15. 彼は発明をあきらめず、私たちの生活に新しくてとても便利な物を作り出したので私は彼を尊敬しています。 |
| 16. The other day, I had a fight with my best friend, Tsubasa at school. | 16. 先日、学校で親友のツバサと喧嘩をしました。 |
| 17. We had a fight because we misunderstood each other. | 17. お互いを誤解してしまったので喧嘩になりました。 |
| 18. When I got home, I felt really bad, so I called him on the phone and said sorry. | 18. 家に帰ってとてもいやな気持ちだったので、電話をして彼に謝りました。 |
| 19. If Bell hadn't invented the telephone, I might not be friends with Tsubasa anymore. | 19. もしベルが電話を発明していなかったら、ツバサともう友達ではなかったかもしれません。 |
| 20. We should all thank the genius Bell for inventing such a brilliant tool. | 20. こんな素晴らしい道具を発明した天才的なベルにみんなで感謝すべきですね。 |
| 21. I think Alexander Graham Bell changed our world the most of anyone in the last two hundred years. | 21. アレクサンダー・グラハム・ベルはここ 200 年で誰よりも私たちの世界を変えたと私は思います。 |
| 22. Thank you, Mr. Bell, and thank you for listening. | 22. ベル、ありがとう。そして皆さん、聞いて頂きましてありがとうございました。 |